SUMMARY

OF

A BEGINNER'S GUIDE

TO THE END

Practical Advice for Living Life
and Facing Death

DR. BJ MILLER & SHOSHANA BERGER

High Speed Reads

TABLE OF CONTENTS

Chapter 1: Don't Leave a Mess 1

Chapter 2: Leave a Mark 3

Chapter 3: Yes, There's Paperwork 5

Chapter 4: Can I Afford to Die? 7

Chapter 5: I'm Sick 9

Chapter 6: Taking Stock 10

Chapter 7: Now What? 12

Chapter 8: Coping 14

Chapter 9: Breaking the News 16

Chapter 10: Love, Sex, and Relationships 18

Chapter 11: Dynamic Duo: Hospice and Palliative Care 20

Chapter 12: Symptoms 101 22

Chapter 13: Hospital Hacks 24

Chapter 14: Help! I Need Somebody 26

Chapter 15: Care for the Caregiver 28

Chapter 16: Everyone Dies: How to Talk to Kids 30

Chapter 17: It's Your Body and Your Funeral 32

Chapter 18: Can I Choose to Die? 34

Chapter 19: Final Days 36

Chapter 20: The First 24 Hours 38

Chapter 21: Grief 40

Chapter 22: How to Write a Eulogy and an Obituary 42

Chapter 23: Celebrating a Life.. 44

Chapter 24: What's Left... 46

Important Facts Recap 47

Analysis & Action Plan 54

Discussion Questions To Get You Thinking 55

About High Speed Reads... 56

CHAPTER 1: DON'T LEAVE A MESS

SUMMARY

Living a life is messy. We end up collecting lots of things as time goes on. But there are more than just physical items to deal with. There's the emotional stuff also.

Sorting through your belongings when you pass is never easy on those left behind. That's why it's recommended that you slowly start clearing out the clutter you've collected. The Swedish call this "Death Cleaning" and it's a practice where an individual clears out all the unnecessary things to make it easier for those who are left. By doing this, you save them time, money and all the heartache they would experience going through your things. Go through each of your items one by one and evaluate if they have any real meaning. If not, toss it.

Another thing to remember is that your loved ones probably don't want your stuff. Some may have small items that they would like to have to remember you by, and others may not be prepared to take anything yet. Those we are wanting to pass items on to may feel as if you are being far too accepting of your fate. Try to be gentle with them and give them time to process.

It's also good to let family and friends come visit so that you can tell them stories about each item that really means something to you. Let them know how you got the necklace you love or the painting that's been hanging on the wall all these years.

You can have everyone come over at once and speak about the items they want, or each can take a turn picking something. Let each person speak about what they want and why while you're still around so that any disputes can be handled ahead of time.

As for the emotional clutter, you need to clear that too. Keep trying to have those conversations that need to be had. Find out how your relationships are doing and try to clear the air. If there are any secrets, be sure to bring them to light. So be sure anything involving other people is mentioned so your loved ones aren't left wondering who the person in the secret box of love letters is.

You can always delegate the job of "cleaner" to one specific person who can go in and remove those incriminating items, if needed. Mend any relationships that need it and remember the pain you caused won't pass when you do. Those left behind will be left with heartache at not mending a relationship with you when you're alive. While they may not be as open as you'd like, it's important you still try.

Recap of chapter 1: Don't Leave a Mess

1. Clear out your stuff for those that you love, so they don't have to.
2. Those left behind experience struggle and heartache when going through their loved one's things.
3. Not all clutter is tangible, some of it's emotional.
4. Fix any relationships that may be strained and get secrets off your chest.

CHAPTER 2: LEAVE A MARK

SUMMARY

Everyone has something to leave behind. Those items you use on a daily basis, any cash you have, stocks, and valuable property can be passed on. If you have enough money, you could create a scholarship or endowment fund.

Another thing to think about is your story. You might think nobody cares, but put yourself in the other persons shoes. How neat would it be to hold a journal from your great great grandmother about life in her time? Tell them everything. Your first crush, your fears, what things were like. Lay it all out on paper so that others can learn about you and experience life through your eyes.

No matter what, you can always leave a mark in some way. You can also write letters to specific people or write out a will explaining why you want each person to have what you're giving them. The thing to remember is that just because you don't feel you have much to offer, doesn't mean that you don't. That one letter or story could mean so much to those left behind when you're gone. Taking a few moments to do so will leave even more memories for them to cherish and let them get a glimpse of the person you wanted them to see.

Recap of chapter 2: Leave a Mark

1. You can always leave money and valuable property to a person or charity.
2. Consider writing down your story so that others can see what your life was like.
3. Writing a letter to loved ones is a great way to be remembered.

CHAPTER 3: YES, THERE'S PAPERWORK

SUMMARY

Unfortunately, it's not a neat and tidy process to die. There are a number of things you may want to have in your "When I Die" file. You will want an advance directive, durable power of attorney for finances, a will and a revocable living trust. Each of these may change as your health does, so don't feel as though they are a one and done deal.

An advance directive is a legal document that lets others know your wishes when it comes to health care if you become terminally ill and can't make decisions for yourself. For most states, this is the same as a living will. Be sure to check the laws for your state for an advance directive because each one is very different.

A durable power of attorney for finances is a form that helps state who can manage your money if you can't. This person should be someone that you trust with your finances, so choose wisely.

A will tells people what to do with your assets and any property you have. You don't have to worry about this if the property has both your name and say your spouse. Then the property would go directly to them.

A revocable living trust is a legal document where you put all of your assets. This can be accounts and properties that you have. With this, there is a trustee that will help manage those assets and make sure that whomever you are giving these things to gets them.

Make sure each of these are in a place that they are easily found and that others know about them. This can make things much easier on your loved ones in the end.

Recap of chapter 3: Yes, There's Paperwork

1. Make sure your plans are down in writing.
2. Check the laws of your state to make sure you're doing it all by the book.
3. Revisit these documents as your health or situation changes.
4. Put all documents in one easy to find place.

CHAPTER 4: CAN I AFFORD TO DIE?

SUMMARY

When you're terminally ill, the bills can add up quickly. Even if you have a nice nest egg, it can quickly become depleted. Even just getting a diagnosis can cost a small fortune. It's important to make sure you have medical insurance to help with the bills and to help pay for medications. Be certain you know exactly what it will cover. Just because the policy costs more, doesn't mean it will cover it all.

There will also be out of pocket costs, even if you have insurance. There are many different "alternative" treatments for example that aren't covered. Neither are things like bed pads or lost wages when you can't work.

Saving money when and where you can will help. You can also open a Health Savings Account which allows you to save for medical expenses. you can also see if there is an "accelerated death benefit" in your life insurance. This allows you to pull money before death. This does come out of what would go to your beneficiaries, but if you need it, it's there. Also, don't forget that hospitals, clinics, etc often are willing to work out payment arrangements.

If you're hoping for Medicaid, make sure you know all the ins and outs. They only give benefits after they've looked five years back at your financial need. If you had more than $2,000 in assets, you may not qualify.

If debt is in your name, your loved ones won't have to take that on. But anything left in your estate will end up going to those bills. So be sure to keep that in mind.

Recap of chapter 4: Can I Afford to Die?

1. Healthcare costs can add up.
2. Make sure you know just what your insurance will cover.
3. Don't rely on Medicaid. There are a lot of rules.
4. Remember that your loved ones won't have to pay your debt but anything in your estate will be applied to it.

CHAPTER 5: I'M SICK

SUMMARY

Finding out you're sick can be like the wind was knocked out of you. For some, it comes without warning while others have some indication. No matter how you find out, it still comes as a shock.

Your brain will start to play tricks on you and you might find it hard processing what the doctor says after your diagnosis. If you're alone, make sure you have someone to drive you home. You may need a moment to sit and gather your thoughts. At some point, you will need to get up and keep moving, but for the moment you might need to allow yourself a moment to process.

Some feel like making rash decisions like getting a divorce or buying a fancy car. For now, you should limit decisions until you can think more clearly. You don't even need to commit to a certain treatment. Not today. Today you need to focus on taking care of yourself and keeping your mind in the right place.

Some of you may have been told this was it only to have things turn around. Others will never get a diagnosis. In this case it's important to listen to what your body is telling you. Think about how you feel versus this time last week. Make decisions based on this.

<u>**Recap of chapter 5: I'm Sick**</u>

1. When you learn of your illness, it's important to take a moment.
2. Don't make any rash decisions just yet.
3. Don't push yourself too hard.

CHAPTER 6: TAKING STOCK

SUMMARY

While some people think the appropriate thing is to turn all decisions over to their doctor, that's not always the case. They don't know what your wishes are. You both need to come up with a personalized plan for your treatment and they need to know who you are to do that. There are a few questions that should be considered.

What have you been doing since being diagnosed? Are you coping well or are you leaning into destructive tendencies? Let them know what's going on so that they can help. You will hopefully have some constructive coping mechanisms to help you through the process.

What have you been thinking about? These are the things that are worrying you and are an indication that changes may need to be made or plans put in place.

What time of day do I feel the best and the worst? Are there places you instantly feel worse when you arrive?

How is your mood? Think about what you've been feeling and why. They may also want to know what you are most proud of or what you like most about yourself. This can help you keep your mind in the right place.

Have you ever lost someone close to you? If so, thinking about their last days can help you make decisions about yours.

When it comes to your treatment, you need to make sure everyone is on the same page. Talk to your doctor about your diagnosis and what you understand about it. Find out what your treatment options are. Speak with them about any symptoms you may be having also.

They should also know if you have people you can or have spoken to about your diagnosis and how they responded. you should also be able to speak freely with your doctor. If you don't feel comfortable you should either fix it or find a new one.

Also, take stock of how you are living and what your assets are. You may need to know sooner than you think. Remember to care for yourself also. This could be simply eating your favorite comfort food and getting lost in a book. Your care should be your first priority.

Recap of chapter 6: Taking Stock

1. Think about what you want when it comes to treatment.
2. Make sure you can speak freely with your doctor and that they listen.
3. Make sure you support your mental health.
4. If you are ever unsure, take a moment to reflect.

CHAPTER 7: NOW WHAT?

SUMMARY

Now that you have a better understanding of your situation, it's time to take action. The thing to remember is that doctors can give you a prognosis, but it's not set in stone. You may wish that it was, but in the end, even the best doctor can't tell you with certainty just how long you have. But when speaking to them about your prognosis, keep these things in mind.

Doctors very rarely underestimate how long a patient has to live. Generally, they overestimate. The better the doctor knows their patient, the more optimistic they tend to be. it's also more accurate when they take into account what it is that you're currently able to do. How much you are eating and how often can make a big difference, for example. You also need to pay attention to how you're feeling most of the time. Lastly, they most likely won't be very specific. It's part of their training not to be.

It's also important to note that you should communicate that if you aren't ready to hear the news your doctor has, that you shouldn't have to. It can really take a toll on your mindset if you hear something you aren't ready for. Stand your ground and let them know just how you want the information presented to you. Some people prefer to know everything and that's fine. But others don't. It should be your choice.

There are also patterns that tend to happen with each illness as it progresses. These are often based solely on physical symptoms, so they can vary of course. You are the only one that can decide what treatment option feels right for you. There are many who choose no treatment. Some may feel as though this is giving up, but that's not the case. Just because you get treatment, doesn't ensure anything. The medical system is designed simply to extend life. It doesn't mean that it will be comfortable. Do what feels right for you.

In the long run, it's important to remember that doctors are only human. They may not have all the answers and you may need to ask certain questions. The important thing is to keep communication open.

Recap of chapter 7: Now What?

1. Your treatment is your choice.
2. Don't let anyone force you into hearing information you aren't ready for.
3. Refusing treatment is not giving up.
4. Remember that doctors are human, too.

CHAPTER 8: COPING

SUMMARY

Death is a very big thing. It can bring up some serious emotions that you have to work your way through. The three that are the most common, however, are denial, grief and fear.

Fear of dying is a very understandable thing. It's not something that can fit neatly in a box like a fear of heights. You can understand that and avoid high places. But everyone dies eventually. But our fear is typically of the dying process. The truth is that dying itself, as conveyed by countless people, is actually peaceful. It may not be for those watching, but it is for the one in the process. Others are afraid of being dead. It suddenly shows that time is limited and all those regrets come to the surface.

Denial is, at its roots, a useful way to cope. After all, it would be hard to function if every day we had to think about our fragile existence. But when others see denial, it is often just a person's way of coming to terms with something on their own time. They may not want to talk about it and prefer to keep going as if nothing had changed.

Grief doesn't have to be later. It can come much sooner than you think. We can grieve the loss of ideas, freedom or bodily functions. Sometimes it's there under everything. It can spring up in the oddest of times, but it's always there.

But there are a few ways to cope. Set goals, enjoy the little things and celebrate the good times. Prayer is always good, too. Be grateful for everything and accept things for what they are.

Love others and let them love you. Try to simply be in the moment and enjoy what you can. Start to work on your creativity and find ways to laugh as often as possible.

<u>Recap of chapter 8: Coping</u>

1. Death is a fear that many of us have.
2. There are many ways you can deal with the reality of death.
3. Live as fully and happily as you can, for as long as you can.

CHAPTER 9: BREAKING THE NEWS

SUMMARY

Telling your loved ones that you are dying can be tough. But often, when you are busy trying to protect them, they are trying to also protect you. When trying to decide who to tell and when, think about who will be the most supportive.

The most important thing is to prepare yourself first. Then, make sure everyone is comfortable and free of distraction. Don't just drop it on them when you start to talk, though. Ease into it by saying something like "I got some tough news from the doctor." After that, let them know what you need from them. Let them have a moment and even listen if necessary. Just like when you were given the news, they may need time to process. No matter what their response, allow it. They may have some misguided responses but they mean well. Try to hear what they are saying beyond their words.

When telling adult children, you may consider not telling them at all. But many feel hurt if you wait too long. They may need the time to process and come to terms. If you don't allow them the ability to be there for you, they may become bitter.

As for your boss, make sure you do it in person and document the meeting. You can also confirm any decisions through email so that there is a paper trail. But beware, some people have prejudices around certain illnesses. This can be good or bad, depending. Know that you don't have to tell your employer anything about your health. While it's a good idea to let them know, you don't have to tell them everything. If after telling them you feel as though you've been discriminated against, you might be covered by the Americans with Disabilities Act.

As for social media, that's a personal decision. Some may feel as though it is a plea for pity, it can also be a great place to get support when you aren't feeling well. Building a blog can also be useful. Not only can you help others in your shoes, but your friends and loved ones can follow how you feel.

Recap of chapter 9: Breaking the News

1. Telling others can be tough, but it's important.
2. Don't put off telling loved ones for too long or they may feel resentful.
3. It's probably best to tell your employer but you aren't legally obligated.
4. Social media can be a useful tool but be mindful of how you use it.

CHAPTER 10: LOVE, SEX, AND RELATIONSHIPS

SUMMARY

Relationships change with illness. Especially our romantic relationships. Some will thrive while others will suffer. The dynamic can change when you are physically incapable of doing those things that you used to do. It's key to allow everyone to grieve the way things were and be open about it. You both should have the ability to get things off your chest, even if the emotions are unpleasant. There are a few things you can do to ensure that you both are able to stick together.

Make sure you still do things together that don't have to do with your illness. Playing a game, watching a movie together, whatever it is you are capable of doing. It can also help to think about those things that first brought you together when your relationship was new. Taking the time to create new rituals or routines can help. Maybe reading aloud to each other or stopping for ice cream after a doctor's appointment. But everything doesn't have to be done together. You both deserve a little alone time also. They deserve to get a break from all the illness and doctor's appointments too. Finally, appreciate one another. Make sure they know just how much you appreciate everything they are doing for you. They may not be sick, but they are right there with you.

Not everyone stays together, however. An already rocky relationship might just come to an end. You may have to find other people to drive you to appointments or find other help from family. The stress of your illness may just be too much for your loved one, and that's okay too.

When it comes to sex, it may depend on your illness as to how much you can handle. For some, it may not be an issue, while for others it could become painful. It's important to have that conversation with your doctor, even if it's awkward. But remember, even if sex is off the table, that doesn't mean you can't still be intimate. Small gestures can feel wonderful and bring a couple closer. Hospital beds may seem like a place you aren't welcome, but there isn't anything wrong with you climbing in bed with them. It's perfectly okay to ask for privacy for a little while and let the nurses know that you'll open the door when you're ready. Be sure to keep communication open with your partner. If something doesn't feel right, let them know. The important thing to remember is that your connection doesn't have to include actual sex. There are many other ways to keep the romance going.

Recap of chapter 10: Love, Sex, and Relationships

1. Talk with your doctor about your illness and how it may affect your sex life.
2. Communicate with your partner any discomfort.
3. Intimacy doesn't have to be just sex.
4. Even if stuck in a hospital or nursing home, you can ask for privacy.

CHAPTER 11: DYNAMIC DUO: HOSPICE AND PALLIATIVE CARE

SUMMARY

Hospice and palliative care are both about making sure all your needs are met. Palliative care is all about the patient and their family in order to help with suffering. It's for any stage of any illness that is serious and is supposed to go along with other treatments. the majority are covered by insurance and can be in the hospital or even at home.

Hospice is for treating the emotional, physical and spiritual discomfort of those who are expected to live six months or less. It's basically palliative care for those at the end of their life. The goal isn't to cure the individual, only to ensure that they are comfortable.

Both kinds of care overlap. Palliative is something that you would have earlier on and hospice comes in at the final stages. It's not all about dying, it's about ensuring that you live well until your time comes. Many don't ask for it early enough or doctors don't refer soon enough simply from misinformation. Often you can have an information interview with a hospice care agency to find out about their service.

It's important to think about hospice early so you can get all its benefits. There are tons of benefits that can really help, depending on your illness. These aren't just medical perks, either. They also help with the emotional and spiritual aspects as well.

Recap of chapter 11: Dynamic Duo: Hospice and Palliative Care

1. Palliative care is for increasing your quality of life and can be implemented anytime in your illness.
2. Hospice is for when you have six months or less and comes to your home.
3. With both, sooner is better.

CHAPTER 12: SYMPTOMS 101

SUMMARY

With illness comes lots of symptoms. Some are from the illness itself and others are from the medications you may be prescribed. For the most part, things that are a discomfort can most often be treated. Of course, with an incurable illness, there will be incurable symptoms. This means that doctors can only get you comfortable enough to help distract you from the symptoms.

Acute symptoms are when they are brief and strong. It's your body's way of communicating that something is wrong. In these times it's important to contact someone right away so that they can help you.

Chronic symptoms happen over time and often persist. These aren't an urgent matter and while they may wear you down, going to the ER won't get results. Those without chronic pain can't possibly understand just how frustrating it can be. It insinuates itself into all aspects of your life and doesn't let up. it can put you in a foul mood and make it hard to function.

In the end, you are the best judge for what is working for you. Some medications just don't work as well as others. You need to find something that will work for you and you don't need to continue to do anything that doesn't help. Sometimes the symptoms are caused by a medication. Yet you are left wondering if it's your disease. The only way to know for sure is to pause the medication and see if the symptom goes away.

Make sure you're tracking your symptoms if you have any. Record the time of day and duration. If it happens at certain times when you are doing something, record that also. Track the severity and if you find anything that makes it better or worse.

Also, don't forget that there are alternative treatments out there. Plenty of people find relief from other means, so it's important to keep an open mind. There are tons of ways that you can help certain symptoms without medication, you just may need to do a bit of research.

Recap of chapter 12: Symptoms 101

1. Only you know if medication is working.
2. Sometimes you may need to experiment to find what works for you.
3. Don't forget that there are alternative treatments that may bring relief.

CHAPTER 13: HOSPITAL HACKS

SUMMARY

If you are stuck going to the hospital, you may find that you need a little help navigating around it all so that you can get the most from it.

Often it starts with a 911 call. The EMTs are supposed to take you to the nearest hospital, but you are allowed to request that you are taken to a different one. You may need to sign a form, however. Once there, the emergency department may make you wait in triage. this will all depend on how busy it is. You may be asked repeatedly what's going on, just take it in stride. They each want to make sure they get it right so there is no error.

Death, however, is not considered an emergency. Those in the emergency room are there to try to fix people. Death can't be fixed, so they may send you home. If you are in the later stages and prefer to be at home when you pass, make sure the doctors there know that.

When packing for the hospital, if you get the chance, there are a few things to keep in mind. Put your name on everything, just so you can keep track of it. Also, listening to music helps reduce stress and pain, so it's good to take something to listen to and some headphones. Have a list of your medications also. make sure you have things to keep you entertained, a change of clothes, including underwear and anything you may want to make you feel more comfortable. Some like to have pictures or other items like that.

It's important that you advocate for yourself, but don't assume you know everything about your disease. Limit your number of questions and make sure they are written down.

Lastly, if you know you are in the end stages of an incurable disease, it's recommended that you have a DNR. This means they will keep you comfortable and that they won't go to extraordinary means to bring you back. This is the best you can hope for in some circumstances. A DNR doesn't mean that doctors will no longer try to help you in general. It just means that if you are dying, they won't resuscitate you.

<u>Recap of chapter 13: Hospital Hacks</u>

1. Understand that emergency rooms don't think an incurable illness is an emergency.
2. If you want to pass at home, make sure your wishes are known.
3. Make sure you speak up and advocate for yourself.

CHAPTER 14: HELP! I NEED SOMEBODY

SUMMARY

In general, people don't want to be a burden when they are sick. They lose their energy, their control and can become highly irritable. So many of us struggle to receive care but have no problem giving it. But there is still plenty you can do, and it's important to not lose that focus. You can still chat with others, make them smile and do what you can to boost their mood. Try to remember that we all need others.

At some point, you may consider hiring a home health aide. They can help with some of the more intimate details you don't want family members to help with, such as going to the bathroom. To hire one, you can go through an agency or hire one yourself or you might have a Medicaid waiver. You know it's time to hire an aide if it's getting harder for you to function around the house and you have issues with some of your daily living activities like eating, bathing or getting dressed.

There is also a home health care program that is geared more toward the medical aspect. This isn't considered an emergency service however. These services include a nurse, a social worker, a therapist for various therapies you may need and a physician that oversees it all.

You may also need a home safety evaluation if you feel as though it's getting tough to do tasks on your own around the home. Things like stairs can be a tripping hazard and require more energy than you may have. But there are some changes that can be made to make things easier.

Improving the lighting to make it easier to see. Making room around your bed if you need to use a wheelchair. Having darker sheets will help hide stains. Getting rid of rugs that make you trip or adding safety mats to slippery floors can make a big difference.

If you do end up with someone helping you, make sure you do your best to help them. Have lists available, help them know what's needed. Your loved ones may need to know your appointments as early as possible or need to know how often you need help with your laundry.

Recap of chapter 14: Help! I Need Somebody

1. Don't be afraid to ask for help.
2. Some help can be hired, look into it as soon as possible.
3. Try to be helpful to those that are helping you.
4. Take measures to make your home safer.

CHAPTER 15: CARE FOR THE CAREGIVER

SUMMARY

Caregiving is both good and bad. It's stressful and taxing both physically and emotionally but can be rewarding as well. Suddenly you can see just how unimportant certain things are like the office gossip or the evening news. Yet it's important to get a chance to step away from it all and breathe.

Sometimes caregivers feel as though they may have something to do with the illness. Maybe if they would have convinced their loved one to stop smoking or eat better then it would have turned out better. But this doesn't help them. If anything, it shifts the attention back to you, where it doesn't belong.

You also have to learn to expect the unexpected. You need to be flexible when you're a caregiver. There are so many things out of your control right now, and out of the person's control that you are caring for. Try to keep reasonable expectations and try again tomorrow.

Caregiving can affect your health as well. You need to remember your own checkups and ensure you exercise and eat properly too. Do your best to unwind, even if it's just taking a trip to the movies. Getting out of the routine of caregiving can break up the monotony.

Just like when flying, you're reminded that you have to put your own oxygen mask on first. The same goes for caregiving. You need to make sure you are taking care of yourself and your needs. Take time to do things you enjoy. Have people you can talk to about everything. Pace yourself and know when you need a distraction. If you start feeling burnt out, find someone to take your place for a little bit. You may end up needing to call hospice. Even having others come in and help you with tasks like grocery shopping or prepping meals can lighten the load.

Recap of chapter 15: Care for the Caregiver

1. Caregivers must take care of themselves first.
2. Know when you need a break.
3. Spend time doing things that bring you peace.
4. Know when you may need to bring in hospice or palliative care.
5. Invite others to help.

CHAPTER 16: EVERYONE DIES: HOW TO TALK TO KIDS

SUMMARY

When dying, there may be children around that are confused. They'll have plenty of questions that you may not be certain you have the answers to.

Often, they want to know if they have to go see their loved one in the hospital. Let them know they don't have to say good-bye there if they don't want. They can draw a picture or write a letter you can deliver. There is no need to hide dying from a child but it's important they are prepared. If there are lots of machines or tubes, let them know ahead of time. Explain that everything there is helping their loved one. Also, allow them to leave if they need to. if they feel overwhelmed, let them sit outside or in the corner. Don't force anything.

Kids also don't always understand death. Cartoons show people coming back or just disappearing, which can be confusing. Ask them what they think will happen or what is going on. They may understand more than you think. They may also wonder if others will die. You can explain that you are there to care for them. That's the main thing they are worried about. Children can be a bit selfish and they want to know someone will be there to protect them.

They may worry they could get sick from being around the sick person. It's important that you explain they will be perfectly fine. Or, they may have been mean to the ill person and fear they caused it. Let them know that it's nobody's fault. It's human nature to want to blame, so blame it on the illness.

If they ask where we go when we die, simply explain that there are lots of different ideas and ask what theirs is. You might be surprised at how incredibly perceptive they can be.

Recap of chapter 16: Everyone Dies: How to Talk to Kids

1. Kids will have lots of questions.
2. Try to explain things simply and directly.
3. Allow them the freedom to be present if they choose.

CHAPTER 17: IT'S YOUR BODY AND YOUR FUNERAL

SUMMARY

A funeral is a highly personal thing and there is nothing wrong with planning your own. You wouldn't hand off your wedding to your sister to plan, your funeral should be no different. Many have started calling them "celebration of life" ceremonies as well. You can hold it wherever you feel is fitting for your service.

If you want a funeral home, go and visit. You'll know instantly if you like it or not. Some have started choosing to have their funeral at home. With this, there is no rush and it's a more comforting place.

Funerals can cost between $7,000 and $10,000. There is a lot to be considered. Funeral homes will tell you what the cost is up front, however. More often than not, they may not allow you to pay ahead of time, but you can put the money aside once it's planned.

Also, don't be afraid to ask questions and if you have a preference, say so. You can choose various caskets, headstones and even what is done with your body.

Traditional burials involve embalming the body with chemicals to preserve it. There are now natural burials where there are no chemicals so you can decompose naturally. Otherwise you can choose cremation. With that, your ashes can be put into items or can even be in the ink of a tattoo.

Another thing to consider is what you will wear when you

are buried. Women should keep in mind their makeup preferences also. Then there are burial plots if you go that route. It's good to look into all of the choices ahead of time so that your funeral is something you would be happy with.

Recap of chapter 17: It's Your Body and Your Funeral

1. It's perfectly reasonable to plan your own funeral.
2. There are plenty of options, so choose carefully.
3. Most places don't allow for prepayment so you may need to put the money aside.
4. Remember to ask questions.

CHAPTER 18: CAN I CHOOSE TO DIE?

SUMMARY

It's an emotional topic, but some want to choose when they die. The US government decided to allow the states to choose themselves, and there are a number where this is now legal. Many choose this option when they don't want to lose themselves to their illness.

Normally this is considered when the person is in constant pain. Some are worried about becoming a burden or are afraid of what is to come. In reality, a third of the people who get the prescription to end their lives don't end up taking it.

If it's something you are considering, it's important to talk to family and doctors about it. Many just want to have the option available to them when and if they feel they need it. If you do go that route, you will need a plan and the law requires doctors to talk to you about a few things. For example, if you have someone that will be there, how it will affect you and so on.

There are a lot of hoops that must be gone through to even choose your death. Even if you manage to find a provider willing to help, there are many rules. Every state is different, so you must check to be certain.

There are alternatives to this, however. Some choose to no longer eat or drink. Since it takes a month to die of starvation, you actually pass from dehydration. Understand that choosing your own death is a very emotional thing for your loved ones. Some may not understand it and may distance themselves. Also, it can be pricey. Your insurance most likely won't cover it so the prescription will be out of pocket.

Recap of chapter 18: Can I Choose to Die?

1. Choosing your death is a very personal decision.
2. Doctors can choose to not give the prescription.
3. Medically sanctioned death is only legal in a few states.
4. You need to be able to take the medication unassisted.

CHAPTER 19: FINAL DAYS

SUMMARY

When a person is actively dying, many describe it as sacred and it certainly feels that way. There will be no more calls to 911, no rushes to the hospital. Now is a time to slow down and pay attention. The process is a profound one and it would be a shame to be distracted from it.

For the most part, the patient will be unconscious, at least to what we in the medical community define consciousness.

There are a few signs death is coming. Confusion, not eating, difficulties breathing, gargling noises, body temperature changes, and incontinence are all signs. You may be present one moment and then somewhere else another. People around you may see you reach for things that aren't there, for example. You may be nice or incredibly mean, it's hard to say. The body will begin to reject food and the hands and feet may start to look mottled. The pulse will be fast, yet faint. Breathing changes and can become fast or labored. Keep in mind that these signs are not all inclusive. Some may be present and others not.

Medications can be given to make the process go easier but some may choose to forgo them. It's important if you don't want these things to let your family and doctor know ahead of time. While many strive to stay conscious, it often doesn't happen. That doesn't mean that the loved one can't hear you, though.

Recap of chapter 19: Final Days

1. The body undergoes a lot of changes when actively dying.
2. There are many physical changes that can be seen when one is dying.
3. If you don't want medications at the end, be sure to let family and physicians know.
4. Understand that just because they aren't conscious, doesn't mean they can't hear you.

CHAPTER 20: THE FIRST 24 HOURS

SUMMARY

In the first 24 hours after someone passes, those left behind feel numb and sometimes so anguished we can't describe it. In this time, you need to do your best to take care of yourself and put one foot in front of the other. Once they have passed there will be a few things that need to be taken care of. These can go in any order you choose, also.

Their death will need to be officially pronounced. You can sit with your loved one for a while if you would like, and you will need to call the funeral home or mortuary. You'll need to contact loved ones at some point. There will also be medications to get rid of and medical equipment to send back. Make sure you also take a break amid all of that.

When it comes to making the death official, if they were receiving hospice care, that's who you should call. They can help you with a few of the steps, if necessary. If they weren't, you'll need to call 911. Explain to them that the death was expected and that you don't want sirens. Make sure you have the DNR or POLST form on hand because the EMTs may try to resuscitate your loved one if there isn't one. This can be tough to watch. If, however, the person is cold or rigor mortis has set in, they should be able to skip the emergency response.

Once everything is done, take some time to relax. eat some comfort food, have a nap, take a walk. Whatever will make you feel better is perfectly okay. Do whatever feels right for you in that moment.

Recap of chapter 20: The First 24 Hours

1. There are only two things that NEED to be done the day you lose your loved one.
2. All that's required is to make the death official and have someone take the body.
3. Take time for yourself and do what feels good for you.
4. Delegate to others if you need some time for yourself.

CHAPTER 21: GRIEF

SUMMARY

In those first few days and weeks, it's hard to say what your emotions will be like. Every person grieves differently, so there is no need to judge yourself. It can seem as if the world should have stopped so when it doesn't it can be jarring.

Sometimes with the death you feel as if you are losing friends when the medical team is required to move on. They can often feel the same way, as they are expected to move to the next patient in need.

Grief will be a strange thing. Sometimes you can feel bitter, angry or even laugh at inappropriate times. You can feel numb or hypersensitive. No matter what, you are changed. Understand that it will look different in everyone. This can help you keep from judging yourself and others too harshly.

You will never be able to "get over" the loss of a loved one. But there are a few things you can do to help. First is to take some time off of work. Not many places offer bereavement leave, but you can usually get 3 to 5 days if it was an immediate family member. Speaking with a member of the clergy or a chaplain can help. Hospice providers also offer bereavement services. You can also find a support group.

If you know someone who is grieving, it can be tough to know what to do. The thing is, they don't know what they need so they can't ask for help. But you can bring them some comfort food or share some pictures of their loved one. If they have children, offer to take them for a bit so they can get away. If you work for the same company, ask if you can give them some of your days off.

Recap of chapter 21: Grief

1. Grief can bring up a variety of responses.
2. Understand that everyone will grieve differently.
3. Reach out if you feel the need to.
4. Take time for self care.

CHAPTER 22: HOW TO WRITE A EULOGY AND AN OBITUARY

SUMMARY

Writing something that feels so important can be daunting. But there are a few guidelines that can help.

In an obituary, include their age, cause, date, and location of death. Their birthdate, parents, partner, and children as well as immediate family that has passed. Include where they went to school, their job, hobbies, pets and all information about the funeral. Make sure you are honest. If the details are whitewashed it can make it difficult for others to understand. Add any bits of humor or surprising details. This can help others know and understand who the person was in life. There may be aspects that are tough, but if it's addressed with respect it can make it easier for everyone else to empathize.

Eulogies are speeches that are given at the memorial or funeral. The important part with these is getting the fullness of the persons life right. Having a diverse set of people to give a eulogy is a great way to see the different sides of a person. If you aren't a close family member and have been asked to speak, know that it's a great honor. If you have been asked, here are some guidelines.

Go for around 1,000 words. Start with a story about them and always write it down. Make sure you are introduced and explain your relationship. Be respectful, but if it suits, add a bit of humor. Be conversational and close with a sentence directed at the person who died. Make sure you show them as they were. Don't try to gloss over the difficult bits.

<u>Recap of chapter 22: How to Write a Eulogy and an Obituary</u>

1. With an obituary, include the cause of death and a bit of personal information.
2. If you aren't family and are asked to give a eulogy, know that it's an honor.
3. Inject a little humor to lighten the mood.
4. Speak truthfully and from the heart.

CHAPTER 23: CELEBRATING A LIFE

SUMMARY

A funeral and a memorial are two very different things. Memorials tend to take place after the burial or cremation. These don't have to be right after the funeral, they can even be a year later. Memorials are for those that are still living. Some prefer to wait until the numbness wears off so that they can really connect to the memorial.

Choose a date and time and decide how much you want to spend. These can either be casual or more formal, depending on the person. Find a venue that suits the mood and make an invitation list. You can choose someone who is the emcee and collect photos and videos of your loved one. Make sure there is food and drinks. Many choose something the person loved in life. You may also want to consider flowers or music.

When it comes to the persons remains, you may choose to scatter the ashes of someone who has been cremated. Know that there are times when this is considered illegal. But there are some places you can do so legally. In city and state parks you can, although you may need a permit. You can do so on public land, at sea or in the air, just as long as you don't drop the container too.

Recap of chapter 23: Celebrating a Life

1. A memorial service can be held a year or more after their death.
2. Choose a service that honors who they were as a person.
3. Use that time as a way to show everyone who they really were.
4. When scattering ashes, know that in some places it's illegal.

CHAPTER 24: WHAT'S LEFT

SUMMARY

There are a few things that will need to be taken care of after your loved one has passed. Eventually there will be need for a headstone or marker if they were buried. The post office will also need to be notified. Forward their mail to someone who can go over it all so the right people can be contacted. Their drivers license needs to be canceled as well as any memberships. Tax professionals also, because their taxes still need paid. Be sure to check online payment services like Paypal for any money. Shut down social media accounts and stop automatic payments. You may need to contact credit card companies and other things like that also.

When it comes to cleaning out their home, there are people who run estate liquidation sales. they can come in and put a price on everything before selling it for you. It can be a huge relief to put that in the hands of another.

Recap of chapter 24: What's Left

1. Make sure mail is forwarded to someone so that places can be contacted.
2. Social media accounts can be closed or memorialized.
3. Cleaning out their home can be done with an estate sale.

IMPORTANT FACTS RECAP

Recap of chapter 1 Don't Leave a Mess

1. Clear out your stuff for those that you love, so they don't have to.
2. Those left behind experience struggle and heartache when going through their loved ones things.
3. Not all clutter is tangible, some of it's emotional.
4. Fix any relationships that may be strained and get secrets off your chest.

Recap of chapter 2 Leave a Mark

1. You can always leave money and valuable property to a person or charity.
2. Consider writing down your story so that others can see what your life was like.
3. Writing a letter to loved ones is a great way to be remembered.

Recap of chapter 3 Yes, There's Paperwork

1. Make sure your plans are down in writing.
2. Check the laws of your state to make sure you're doing it all by the book.
3. Revisit these documents as your health or situation changes.
4. Put all documents in one easy to find place.

Recap of chapter 4 Can I Afford to Die?

1. Healthcare costs can add up.
2. Make sure you know just what your insurance will cover.
3. Don't rely on Medicaid. There are a lot of rules.
4. Remember that your loved ones won't have to pay your debt but anything in your estate will be applied to it.

Recap of chapter 5 I'm Sick

1. When you learn of your illness, it's important to take a moment.
2. Don't make any rash decisions just yet.
3. Don't push yourself too hard.

Recap of chapter 6 Taking Stock

1. Think about what you want when it comes to treatment.
2. Make sure you can speak freely with your doctor and that they listen.
3. Make sure you support your mental health.
4. If you are ever unsure, take a moment to reflect.

Recap of chapter 7 Now What?

1. Your treatment is your choice.
2. Don't let anyone force you into hearing information you aren't ready for.
3. Refusing treatment is not giving up.
4. Remember that doctors are human, too.

Recap of chapter 8 Coping

1. Death is a fear that many of us have.
2. There are many ways you can deal with the reality of death.
3. Live as fully and happily as you can, for as long as you can.

Recap of chapter 9 Breaking the News

1. Telling others can be tough, but it's important.
2. Don't put off telling loved ones for too long or they may feel resentful.
3. It's probably best to tell your employer but you aren't legally obligated.
4. Social media can be a useful tool but be mindful of how you use it.

Recap of chapter 10 Love, Sex, and Relationships

1. Talk with your doctor about your illness and how it may affect your sex life.
2. Communicate with your partner any discomfort.
3. Intimacy doesn't have to be just sex.
4. Even if stuck in a hospital or nursing home, you can ask for privacy.

Recap of chapter 11 Dynamic Duo: Hospice and Palliative Care

1. Palliative care is for increasing your quality of life and can be implemented anytime in your illness.

2. Hospice is for when you have six months or less and comes to your home.
3. With both, sooner is better.

Recap of chapter 12 Symptoms 101

1. Only you know if medication is working.
2. Sometimes you may need to experiment to find what works for you.
3. Don't forget that there are alternative treatments that may bring relief.

Recap of chapter 13 Hospital Hacks

1. Understand that emergency rooms don't think an incurable illness is an emergency.
2. If you want to pass at home, make sure your wishes are known.
3. Make sure you speak up and advocate for yourself.

Recap of chapter 14 Help! I Need Somebody

1. Don't be afraid to ask for help.
2. Some help can be hired, look into it as soon as possible.
3. Try to be helpful to those that are helping you.
4. Take measures to make your home safer.

Recap of chapter 15 Care for the Caregiver

1. Caregivers must take care of themselves first.
2. Know when you need a break.
3. Spend time doing things that bring you peace.

4. Know when you may need to bring in hospice or palliative care.
5. Invite others to help.

Recap of chapter 16 Everyone Dies: How to Talk to Kids

1. Kids will have lots of questions.
2. Try to explain things simply and directly.
3. Allow them the freedom to be present if they choose.

Recap of chapter 17 It's Your Body and Your Funeral

1. It's perfectly reasonable to plan your own funeral.
2. There are plenty of options, so choose carefully.
3. Most places don't allow for prepayment so you may need to put the money aside.
4. Remember to ask questions.

Recap of chapter 18 Can I Choose to Die?

1. Choosing your death is a very personal decision.
2. Doctors can choose to not give the prescription.
3. Medically sanctioned death is only legal in a few states.
4. You need to be able to take the medication unassisted.

Recap of chapter 19 Final Days

1. The body undergoes a lot of changes when actively dying.
2. There are many physical changes that can be seen when one is dying.
3. If you don't want medications at the end, be sure to let

family and physicians know.

4. Understand that just because they aren't conscious, doesn't mean they can't hear you.

Recap of chapter 20 The First 24 Hours

1. There are only two things that NEED to be done the day you lose your loved one.
2. All that's required is to make the death official and have someone take the body.
3. Take time for yourself and do what feels good for you.
4. Delegate to others if you need some time for yourself.

Recap of chapter 21 Grief

1. Grief can bring up a variety of responses.
2. Understand that everyone will grieve differently.
3. Reach out if you feel the need to.
4. Take time for self care.

Recap of chapter 22 How to Write a Eulogy and an Obituary

1. With an obituary, include the cause of death and a bit of personal information.
2. If you aren't family and are asked to give a eulogy, know that it's an honor.
3. Inject a little humor to lighten the mood.
4. Speak truthfully and from the heart.

Recap of chapter 23 Celebrating Life

1. A memorial service can be held a year or more after their death.
2. Choose a service that honors who they were as a person.
3. Use that time as a way to show everyone who they really were.
4. When scattering ashes, know that some places it's illegal.

Recap of chapter 24 What's Left

1. Make sure mail is forwarded to someone so that places can be contacted.
2. Social media accounts can be closed or memorialized.
3. Cleaning out their home can be done with an estate sale.

ANALYSIS & ACTION PLAN

With this book, "A Beginners Guide to the End: Practical Advice for Living Life and Facing Death" I feel like the stigma of death is brought to light. Right from the beginning, the book is very straight forward and honest. Telling it all like it is without a bunch of frivolous words or pretty sentences. Starting right from the beginning at finding out you are terminally ill, this book will walk it's reader through everything a terminally ill patient and their family would ever need to know.

Breaking down the barriers of speaking about death, here you can learn about everything from the paperwork to the conversations you should be having. The author not only tells you stories from their own experience but those that they have dealt with in their practice. It's very reassuring to hear what you should be expecting and helps bring a bit of normalcy to something that can be so very chaotic.

For anyone who has a loved one who is terminal, this book lays out exactly what you should expect. This is something that was done with great detail and care. I believe that this should be standard reading for anyone who is terminally diagnosed or caring for someone who is. Great care went into explaining everything that needs to be done after, with emphasis on being gentle with yourself and others. It's exactly what it says it is, a beginner's guide to the end.

DISCUSSION QUESTIONS TO GET YOU THINKING

1. Have you ever cared for someone that was terminally ill?

2. What ways have your loved ones that passed left their mark on you?

3. Have you had someone break the news to you that they were terminally ill?

4. In your experience, does illness bring people together or push them apart?

5. Have you ever dealt with hospice or palliative care?

6. If you have ever stayed in a hospital, what was your experience?

7. When do you feel people should start to receive help?

8. Have you or someone you know ever been a caregiver?

9. What are your views on choosing to die?

10. Have you been in the room when someone passed? What was your experience like?

ABOUT HIGH SPEED READS

Here at High Speed Reads our goal is to save you time by providing the best summaries possible. We stand out from our competitors by not only including all of the pertinent facts from the subject book but also a personal analysis of the book with action plan included, easy to follow summaries of each chapter including a list of chapter highlights and even discussion questions to get you thinking.

As you can see we go above and beyond to make your purchase a pleasant one. If you learned something beneficial from this book please leave a positive review so others can benefit as well. Lastly if you haven't yet make sure you purchase the subject book, A Beginner's Guide to the End, by visiting
https://amzn.to/2YDslm4